Safari
ACROSS AMERICA
- a travel journal -

This journal belongs to:

Centennial Media Center
13200 Westlake Dr.
Broomfield, CO 80020

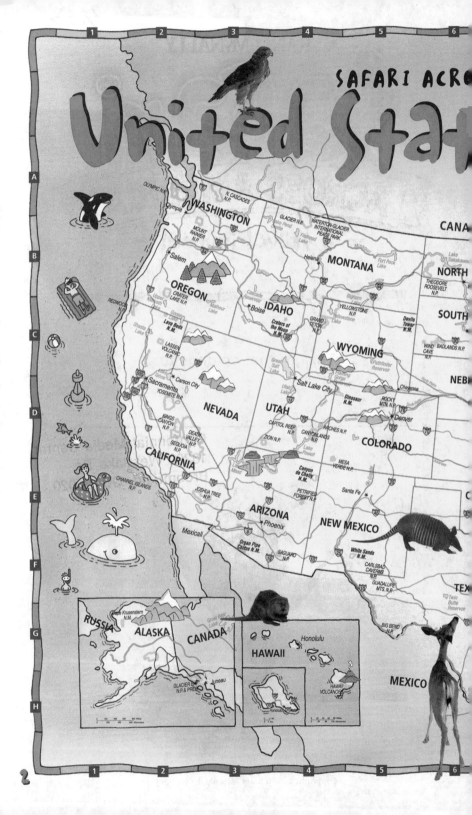

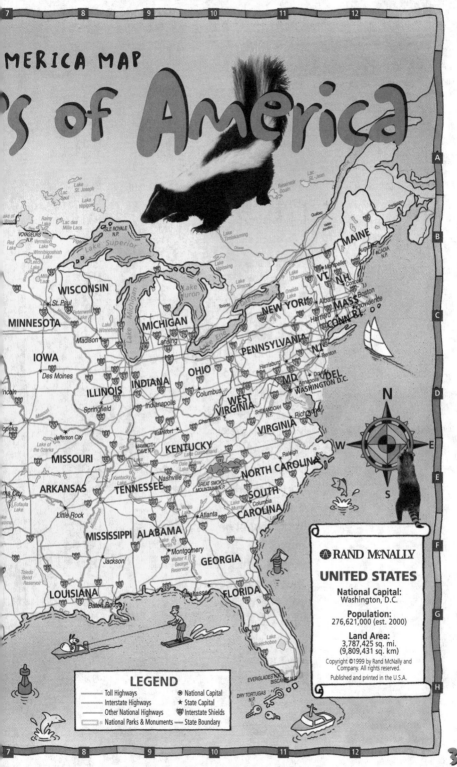

America's National Parks

EASTERN

– United States –

Everglades National Park

EASTERN

UNITED STATES

NATIONAL PARKS

1. **Acadia, ME**
   More than 300 species of birds call this beautiful combination of mountains and seashore home.

2. **Biscayne, FL**
   Most of this park lies under water!

3. **Everglades, FL**
   Alligators and waterfowl live together in a delicate ecosystem.

4. **Great Smoky Mountains, TN/NC**
   The busiest U.S. national park.

5. **Isle Royale, MI**
   The only way to get to this park is by boat or float-plane.

6. **Mammoth Cave, KY**
   Visitors can explore the world's largest known cave system.

7. **Shenandoah, VA**
   Deer, bears, and bobcats can be found here.

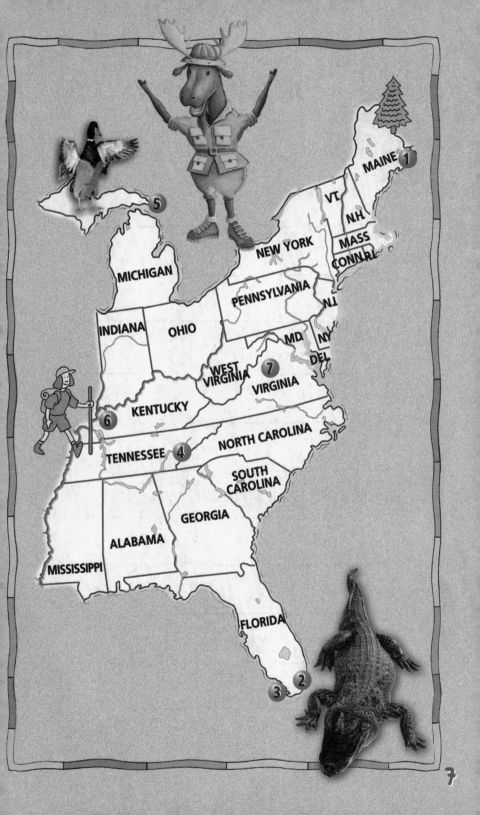

MAINE ①

VT.

N.H.

MASS

CONN R.I.

NEW YORK

PENNSYLVANIA

N.J.

MICHIGAN

INDIANA OHIO

MD.

N.Y.

DEL

WEST VIRGINIA ⑦

VIRGINIA

⑥ KENTUCKY

TENNESSEE ④ NORTH CAROLINA

SOUTH CAROLINA

GEORGIA

ALABAMA

MISSISSIPPI

FLORIDA

⑤

③ ②

Travel Journal

Today I saw:

_____

_____

_____

_____

_____

_____

_____

_____

_____

_____

I'm really looking forward to this:

_____

_____

_____

_____

_____

_____

_____

_____

_____

_____

_____

Best Vacation Ever!

Create your own crazy story about your vacation. Ask somebody for words to fill in the blanks below. Then read the story aloud.

_____ says that the best vacation ever is a _____
person's name noun

trip to_____. Once you're there, you just have to_____.
place verb

And don't forget to_____. The most exciting things to do are
verb

_____and _____ , but only if you're wearing
an activity an activity

_____. There's _____ food to eat, too.
type of clothing adjective

Order the_____ and _____ special for a real treat.
noun noun

Tell them_____ sent you. Before you head home,
person's name

be sure to buy a_____at the souvenir shop! It will always
noun

remind you of your_____ trip.
adjective

Things I'll tell my friends about:

_____

_____

_____

_____

_____

_____

_____

_____

_____

_____

_____

Hey! Guess where I've been!

TO: _____

Safari Mail!

Every vacation needs at least one great postcard to send home. On one side of the postcard, write all about your trip. On the other side, draw a picture about it.

Everglades National Park

Snakes, pelicans, and gators, oh my!

See if you can solve these puzzles about the Everglades.
The first one is done for you.

GAL. − G + 👁 + 〰️ + ✖ = alligator

+ You Owe $10.⁰⁰ =

− H + 🎀 + T =

+ 🌾 =

C + 🌧️ ← =

T + 👗 − SK + L =

SN + 🧹 − R =

Find the answers on the inside back cover.

Sometimes I got
mad when:

_____

_____

_____

_____

_____

_____

_____

_____

_____

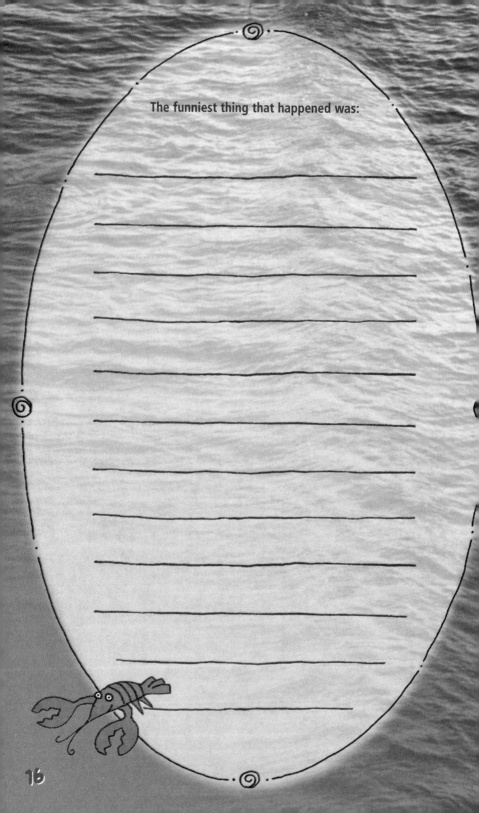

The funniest thing that happened was:

_____

_____

_____

_____

_____

_____

_____

_____

_____

_____

_____

Draw a picture or put in a photo
of your favorite place!

The best part about taking a trip:

_____

_____

_____

_____

_____

_____

_____

_____

_____

_____

_____

_____

I can't believe that:

_____

_____

_____

_____

_____

_____

_____

_____

_____

_____

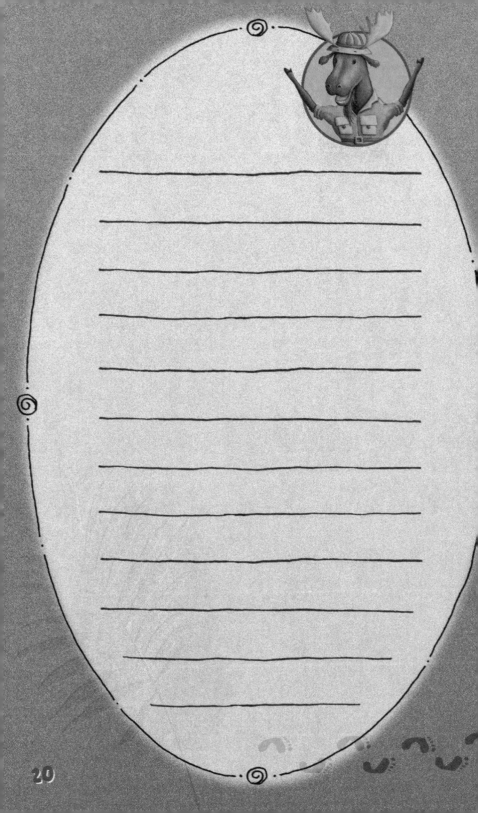

CENTRAL

– United States –

Badlands National Park

CENTRAL

UNITED STATES

NATIONAL PARKS

• •

1. Badlands, SD
Fantastic, colorful rock formations can be found in this park. The Badlands earns its name with extremes of summer and winter.

2. Big Bend, TX
Desert, river, and mountains can all be explored at Big Bend.

3. Guadalupe Mountains, TX
Mule deer, raccoons, mountain lions, and black bears roam the park.

4. Theodore Roosevelt, ND
Named for the former president, this park boasts colorful rock formation and extremely dry land.

5. Voyageurs, MN
This is the only region in the continental U.S. that supports eastern timber wolves.

6. Wind Cave, SD
Bison, elk, and pronghorn graze the land.

NORTH DAKOTA

SOUTH DAKOTA

NEBRASKA

KANSAS

OKLAHOMA

TEXAS

MINNESOTA

IOWA

MISSOURI

ARKANSAS

LOUISIANA

WISCONSIN

ILLINOIS

I've always wanted to go to:

_____

_____

_____

_____

_____

_____

_____

_____

_____

_____

_____

Travel Journal

Exploring is great because:

_____

_____

_____

_____

_____

_____

_____

_____

_____

_____

_____

_____

Travel Safari

Create your own crazy story about your vacation. Ask somebody for words to fill in the blanks below. Then read the story aloud.

It was a _____ night and the_____ family
    adjective   person's last name

was driving down the highways on its way to_____.
                                                      place

All of of a sudden, they saw _____ _____
                                  number   plural noun

along the side of the highway. They decided to _____
                                                          verb

because it seemed like the right thing to do. _____ decided
                                                    person's name

to call for a little _____ and everyone else started
                          noun

_____. When the _____ arrived, every-
    -ing word   noun

thing was under control. A passerby said, "It certainly was luck that

this _____ family was driving by. Those kids knew
          adjective

exactly what to do in a _____ like this." The kids admit-
                              noun

ted, "We were _____ , and it was a great adven-
                    adjective

ture, but now we have to get _____."
                                    -ing word

26

The worst part about going on a trip:

_____

_____

_____

_____

_____

_____

_____

_____

_____

_____

_____

Safari Mail!

TO: _____
_____
_____

Wow! You won't believe what happened today!

Black Hills

Gold Mining!

Find the six hidden things in these mountains.
(Hint: There's gold in them thar hills!)

For answers, see the inside back cover

Travel Journal

If I found a bag of gold I would:

_____

_____

_____

_____

_____

_____

_____

_____

_____

_____

_____

_____

Travel Journal

Here's the cool stuff I saw today:

_____

_____

_____

_____

_____

_____

_____

_____

_____

_____

_____

_____

Draw a picture of two animals mixed together. For example, what would a wormigator or a frogoose look like?

We had a close call when:

_____

_____

_____

_____

_____

_____

_____

_____

_____

_____

_____

I felt proud of myself when:

_____

_____

_____

_____

_____

_____

_____

_____

_____

_____

_____

_____

Travel Journal

NORTHWEST

- United States -

Yellowstone National Park

NORTHWEST

UNITED STATES

NATIONAL PARKS

1. **Crater Lake, OR**
   Crater Lake is the deepest lake in the U.S.

2. **Denali, AK**
   This park is home to Mt. McKinley and wildlife such as caribou, moose, and beaver.

3. **Glacier, MT**
   Grizzly bear, moose, and otter can be found at Glacier National Park.

4. **Glacier Bay, AK**
   Whales are a common sight in the waters of this park.

5. **Grand Teton, WY**
   In this mountainous park bald eagles, buffalo, and elk can be seen.

6. **Mt. Rainier, WA**
   The centerpiece of this park is Mt. Rainier, which stands over 14,000 feet tall.

7. **North Cascades, WA**
   There are more than 300 glaciers in this park!

8. **Olympic, WA**
   Temperate rain forest, coastline, and mountains can all be found in this diverse park

9. **Yellowstone, WY**
   The most famous sight at this park is the geyser known as Old Faithful.

ALASKA

WASHINGTON

OREGON

MONTANA

IDAHO

WYOMING

Travel Journal

The best travel companion would be:

_____

_____

_____

_____

_____

_____

_____

_____

_____

_____

_____

_____

The most exciting thing that happened was:

_____

_____

_____

_____

_____

_____

_____

_____

_____

_____

_____

_____

Well, I was a Little Scared

Create your own crazy story about your vacation.
Ask somebody for words to fill in the blanks below.
Then read the story aloud.

It was a _____ night for ghost stories. _____
           adjective   person's name

complained that it would be too spooky, but I thought it would be fun.

The campfire was _____ and a chill was in the air. My story
                  -ing word

was called "The _____ Campsite". As I started to talk I heard
                 adjective

a noise in the woods. To me it sounded exactly like a _____.
                                                        noun

I was sure it was nothing and strarted again. We heard the noise again,

only this time it was louder, and it was followed by a voice. "Who?"

We all sat still. "Who's there?" _____ asked. Instead of
                                  person's name

an answer we heard a "Who?" Needless to say we _____
                                                 verb (past tense)

as fast as we could. Just when we thought we couldn't _____
                                                        verb

anymore we saw the beam of a flashlight. "Are you kids okay?" It was

_____, the park ranger. "I was out practicing my _____
person's name   -ing word

owl calls when I saw you kids running," he said. We all laughed at our

mistake and went back to our campsite. We got back to camp and I had

a great idea for a story. I called it "The _____ Ranger and
                                            -ing word

his _____ owl calls." Everyone acted like they didn't want
     adjective

to hear it, but I told the _____ story anyway.
                            adjective

You would never believe this:

_____

_____

_____

_____

_____

_____

_____

_____

_____

_____

_____

afari Mail!

n't wait to do this again!

Denali National Park
Midnight Sun!

Find and circle these things you can see in Denali.

Arctic Warbler	Golden Plover	Moose	Snowshoe Hare
Bear	Grebe	Mountain Goat	Spruce
Beaver	Grizzly Bear	Mount McKinley	Squirrel
Caribou	Hill	Otter	Tern
Cliff	Ice	Pika	Valley
Cub	Log	Ptarmigan	Wheatear
Dall Sheep	Long-tailed Jaeger	Raven	Wolf
Fox	Loon	River	Wolverine
Glacier	Lynx	Rock	
Golden Eagle	Marmot	Snow Bunting	

L	O	O	N	G	G	N	I	T	N	U	B	W	O	N	S
L	O	N	N	A	G	I	M	R	A	T	P	O	W	P	R
E	O	N	R	A	S	Q	U	I	R	R	E	L	H	E	T
Y	N	G	G	E	O	R	E	V	I	R	L	V	E	E	A
E	R	R	O	T	T	E	R	A	T	I	T	E	A	H	R
L	E	E	Y	L	A	H	K	E	H	A	R	R	T	S	C
N	L	B	E	N	D	I	E	S	O	O	M	I	E	L	T
I	G	E	L	A	P	E	L	G	D	R	N	N	A	L	I
K	A	L	L	E	V	E	N	E	M	F	E	E	R	A	C
C	E	R	A	E	C	I	U	P	D	A	F	V	V	D	W
M	N	A	V	C	A	U	C	O	L	J	R	I	A	A	A
T	E	E	F	T	I	U	R	Y	B	O	A	M	L	E	R
N	D	B	N	L	B	E	N	P	N	I	V	E	O	C	B
U	L	U	T	F	O	X	R	U	S	R	R	E	G	T	L
O	O	E	S	N	O	W	S	H	O	E	H	A	R	E	E
M	G	R	I	Z	Z	L	Y	B	E	A	R	O	C	K	R

Look on the inside back cover for answers.

Travel Journal

The day I didn't want to end was:

_____

_____

_____

_____

_____

_____

_____

_____

_____

Travel Journal

Next time I don't want to miss:

Draw a picture of what it would be like to live under water!

I was so bored when:

Travel Journal

If I had a time machine I'd go:

_____

_____

_____

_____

_____

_____

_____

_____

_____

_____

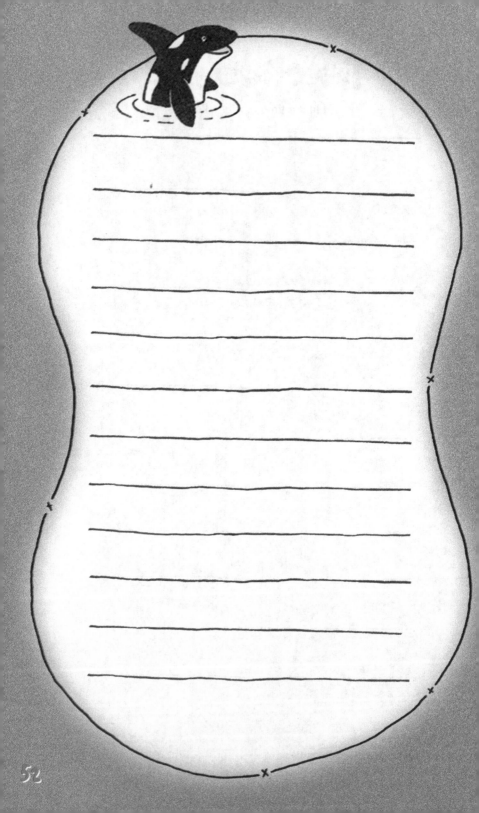

WESTERN
- United States -

WESTERN

UNITED STATES

NATIONAL PARKS

• •

1. **Carlsbad Caverns, NM**
   More than one million bats can be found in the caverns.

2. **Grand Canyon, AZ**
   Porcupines, lizards, and snakes roam the enormous canyon.

3. **Hawaii Volcanoes, HI**
   This park is home to Kilauea, the world's most active volcano.

4. **King's Canyon/Sequoia,CA**
   The Giant Forest of sequoias is home to the General Sherman tree, the world's largest tree at over 250 feet!

5. **Mesa Verde, CO**
   Formed in 1906, it was the very first National Park.

6. **Rocky Mountain, CO**
   In some parts of the park there are plants that can only be found in one other place, the Arctic!

7. **Yosemite, CA**
   This park is about the same size as the state of Rhode Island.

8. **Zion, UT**
   The Zion snail is found in only one place in the world — right there in Zion National Park.

9. **Arches, UT**
   Sandstone arches are the major attraction at this park.

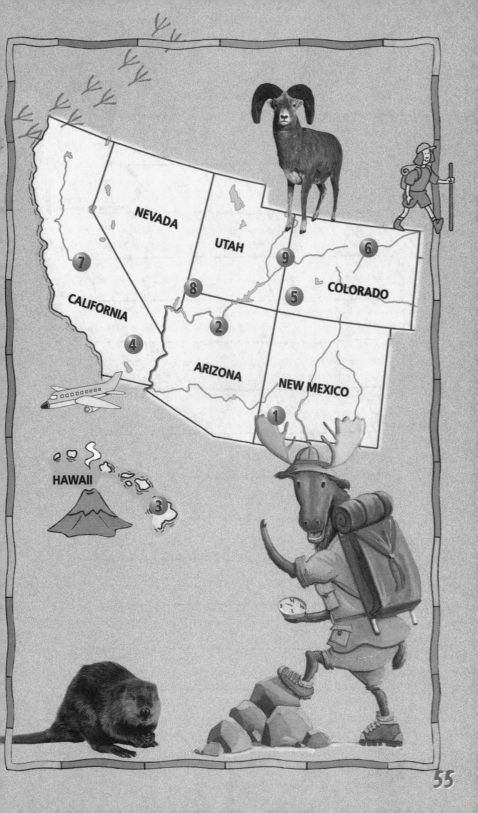

NEVADA

UTAH

CALIFORNIA

COLORADO

ARIZONA

NEW MEXICO

HAWAII

On a bright, sunny day, I like to:

_____

_____

_____

_____

_____

_____

_____

_____

_____

_____

_____

The absolute worst thing I've done so far:

_____

_____

_____

_____

_____

_____

_____

_____

_____

_____

_____

DEAD
END

TRUE STORY

Create your own crazy story about your vacation.
Ask somebody for words to fill in the blanks below.
Then read the story aloud.

Feeling adventurous, I decided to try and climb the _____ _____ .
                                                    adjective   noun

It would be a dangerous journey, so I would need to take along my

trusted companion, _____. We began in the morning after a
                    person's name

_____ meal of_____ . It was delicious! We
    adjective   noun

gathered our gear and set out towards the_____ . Before we took
                                              noun

_____step(s) a storm came up. It was the worst one I'd ever
  a number

seen. "Yowzer, this is bad", I yelled. "Let's get _____ before
                                                    -ing word

it's too late!" It's a good thing we did because just at that moment

_____ came _____ by our heads. "Take cover!"
  plural noun   -ing word

The wind was incredible, swirling and _____ around us. The
                                          -ing word

_____storm passed quickly, but all of our gear was gone,
    adjective

even the_____. I was very upset. I slowly realized that we had
            noun

been swept up in the winds and been plopped on top of the very

_____ I had wanted to climb. Every word of my story is true.
    noun

58

If I could have three wishes, I would wish for:

1 _____

_____

_____

_____

2 _____

_____

_____

3 _____

_____

_____

_____

Safari Mail!

Wow! You won't believe
what happened today!

TO:

DEAD
END

61

Hop aboard a mule and ride down into the Grand Canyon

See if you can find the way.

The goofiest person I met was:

_____

_____

_____

_____

_____

_____

_____

_____

_____

_____

**My favorite way
to travel is:**

_____

_____

_____

_____

_____

_____

_____

_____

_____

_____

_____

Draw yourself (or someone you know) as an animal.

The neatest animal I've seen is:

_____

_____

_____

_____

_____

_____

_____

_____

_____

_____

_____

_____

A beautiful sunset makes me think of:

_____

_____

_____

_____

_____

_____

_____

_____

_____

_____

_____

_____

If I could go anywhere in the U.S., it would be:

BACKYARD SAFARI

~ Taking a closer look! ~

Your Backyard

Draw Your Own Backyard

Draw your backyard in as much detail as possible.
Include everything you can to give Milo a great
place to explore.

Look around! See how many of these animals you can find around your backyard!

My favorite place to explore is:

_____

_____

_____

_____

_____

_____

_____

_____

_____

_____

_____

When I'm outside, I like to collect:

_____

_____

_____

_____

_____

_____

_____

_____

_____

_____

_____

_____

Backyard Explorers

Create your own crazy story about your vacation.
Ask somebody for words to fill in the blanks
below. Then read the story aloud.

Because I hadn't cut the grass in a while, the backyard looked like a

_____ jungle. The blades reached pretty high, taller than
　　　adjective

a _____ . And that's tall, let me tell you. _____
　　noun　　　　　　　　　　　　　　　　　　　　　　　person's name

had spent the night, so we decided to go outside and play with the

_____ . _____ threw it far over my head and I had to
　noun　　　　person's name

chase it into the _____ grass. I didn't find the _____ ,
　　　　　　　　　　adjective　　　　　　　　　　　　　noun

but I did see _____ . Needless to say, I _____ .
　　　　　　　plural nouns　　　　　　　　　　　　　　verb (past tense)

_____ didn't believe me, so we went looking together. We found a
person's name

_____ , a _____ , and a _____ . This was
　noun　　　　　　　　noun　　　　　　　　　adjective noun

getting exciting! The rest of the afternoon we spent _____
　　　　　　　　　　　　　　　　　　　　　　　　　　　　　　-ing word

just in case someone came by and saw all of this great stuff. This

search went on all summer. We put all of the stuff in a big pile, even

the _____ which I hadn't seen in years. You'd think that after I got
　　noun

lost for _____ hours I would've cut the grass. I didn't, we just
　　　number more than one

decided it was easier to move. What happened to all of that stuff, you

might ask? Let's just say _____ and I had the _____ garage sale
　　　　　　　　　　　person's name　　　　　　　　　adjective

the world had ever seen. By the way, do you want to buy a _____ ?
　　　　　　　　　　　　　　　　　　　　　　　　　　　　　　noun

**My favorite part
of the neighborhood:**

_____

_____

_____

_____

_____

_____

_____

_____

_____

_____

_____

_____

Wow! You w

Safari Mail!

ve what happened today!

If I could have someone come to visit, it would be:

_____

_____

_____

_____

_____

_____

_____

_____

_____

_____

_____

If I could live next door to anyone I wanted:

_____

_____

_____

_____

_____

_____

_____

_____

_____

_____

_____

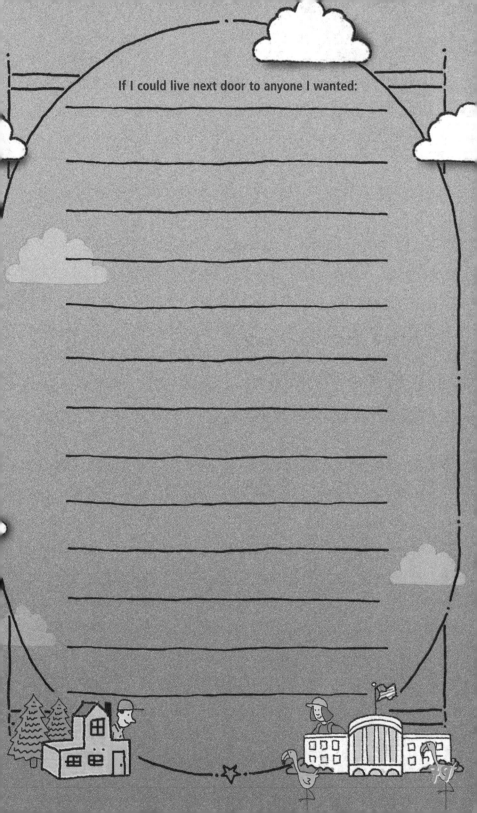